This book is dedicated to my grandchildren:
Ashtian, Abigail, and Mollie.

They are the children of
Mark and Laura Gumm.

Their father, Mark, passed away on March 24, 2014. When their mother told them about his passing, the heartbreak in their eyes was unimaginable. Five years later, on July 12, 2019, I had to tell them that their only living parent, Laura, had also passed away from a traumatic seizure. These three precious children experienced tragedy at such a young age.

This book is for the children that have faced the painful feelings that come with the death of a parent. My hope is that all children dealing with the pain of loss will have a strong support system who can help them recognize and feel the presence of God.

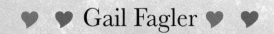 Gail Fagler

It takes a village to raise a child.
This is an adage proved to be true.

This book is dedicated to:
Ashtian, Abigail, and Mollie.

These three precious children were left without parents
at such a young and fragile age.

My hope is that this book will serve as a part of the healing
process for children dealing with the tragic loss of a parent.

Through the pain of unimaginable loss,
these children have brought unmatched joy to the lives of
me and my husband, Mike.

We believe in the beauty of God's plan and hope this book
will help others see light in each struggle.

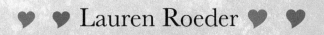 ♥ ♥ Lauren Roeder ♥ ♥

VESTRA LINGUA KIDS

VLK

Story © 2021
Gail Fagler and Lauren Roeder
Illustrations © 2021 Lintang Pandu

All Rights Reserved.
FIRST EDITION.
ISBN: HARDBACK ISBN 978-1-950574-17-9
SOFTBACK ISBN 978-1-950574-18-6

Library of Congress Control Number Applied For

JUV033100 JUVENILE FICTION / Religious / Christian / Family Life
JUV033240 JUVENILE FICTION / Religious / Christian / Values & Virtues
JUV039030 JUVENILE FICTION / Social Themes / Death, Grief, Bereavement

Questions? Comments? We love feedback: info@vestralingua.com

Need information about licensing, custom editions, bulk sales, or academic/corporate purchases? Write the publisher at the address below.

VESTRA LINGUA KIDS
C/o Vestra Lingua LLC
PO Box 2594
West Columbia, SC 29171

WWW.VESTRALINGUA.COM

Mom & Dad are in Heaven (I'm Only Seven)

Written by:
Gail Fagler and
Lauren Roeder

My name is Mollie.

I am seven years old.

I love the color pink, and I love playing dress-up.

I like playing with my friends and riding my bike.

Most of all, I love my family.
I have a sister named Abby and
a brother named Ashtian.
My daddy's name is Mark,
and my mommy's name is Laura.

My daddy went to Heaven when I was only two. He had an awful sickness called cancer. I was too little to wonder what would happen next. I know that my daddy is in heaven and that he is looking down on me. He sends his love to me every single day. My daddy is an angel.

My mommy was sad after my daddy went to heaven. Still, she loved me very much. She would hold me and play with me.

She would tell me about my daddy and show me pictures of him. She missed my daddy every single day.

In her mind, she wondered,
"What will happen next?"

Soon, we moved in with Grandma.
She took care of my siblings and me.

Five years went by.
We stayed with Grandma and
made a happy home.

Still, I knew my mommy was missing my daddy.

One day, my mommy got very sick. She was having a lot of seizures. The next thing I knew, she was in heaven with Jesus and my daddy.

I am only seven and life is changing again.
Sometimes I wonder to myself, "What will happen next?"

Now, my mommy and my daddy
are in heaven.

I don't know what to do!
Who will take care of me?
Where will I live?
What will I do?
I am only seven!
I begin to wonder,
"What will happen next?"

Grandma was there to hold me.
She told me everything would be okay.

Our friends and family came to our home and helped us after my mommy died.
Even people I didn't know helped us.

I know there are a lot of people who love me.
They will help care for me along the way.
It's very scary to be seven years old without a mommy
or daddy here with me.

I know my mommy would tell me to, "Trust in Jesus."

That's what she always said.
Grandma says that God cares
for us.
He already knows what will
happen next.

The people that love us have stepped up to say,
"We will help you along the way."

I may be only seven, but I know God is with me.
He keeps my family and me safe and happy.
He brought so many people that loved me so much
to help take care of me.
Still, I wonder, "What will happen next?"

I don't have to wonder anymore.
God is showing me the way.
My mommy and daddy are happy.
They are in Heaven with Jesus.
That makes me happy too!

I am only seven but I know they are looking down on me and smiling.

I even released two balloons to Heaven to tell them I will love them forever.

Even though I'm only seven, I know what Grandma says is true.
She tells me every day, "Pray and trust in God. He will walk
before you and prepare a future for you."

I no longer have to wonder, "What will happen next?"

2 Corinthians 5:7

For we live by faith, not by sight.

About Lauren

Lauren Roeder

Lauren Roeder is the co-author of <u>Mom & Dad are in Heaven (I'm only Seven.)</u> She studied Broadcast Journalism and Business Management at the University of South Carolina. She chose her career based on her passion for writing. Lauren spent several years working as a News Producer at WYFF News 4 in Greenville, South Carolina. She determined and wrote story content for the weekday morning shows. She also spent time writing breaking and developing news stories for the station's website and social media pages.

Lauren currently works at the South Carolina Department of Transportation as a Public Information Coordinator. She serves as a Media Liaison, sharing vital information with the media and the public. In her role at SCDOT, Lauren is an administrator for the Facebook and Twitter pages. She reports and posts about road and bridge projects throughout South Carolina.

In her spare time, Lauren volunteers for Hidden Wounds, a non-profit organization based in Columbia. Hidden Wounds provides peace of mind and comfort for military personnel battling combat stress injuries such as post-traumatic stress, traumatic brain injury, and other psychological post-war challenges. Lauren serves as a Social Media Strategist for the non-profit. She writes strategic messages to promote Hidden Wounds. She also trains other employees and volunteers to strategically post in order to get more traffic to the organization's website and social media pages.

Lauren lives in Columbia, South Carolina. She grew up in Chapin and attended Chapin High School. She knew from a young age that she had a passion for writing. A family tragedy inspired her to write this book in hopes that it would bring about peace and healing.

ABOUT GAIL

Gail Fagler

Gail Fagler is the co-author of <u>Mom & Dad are in Heaven (I'm Only Seven.)</u> She has a passion for helping children grow through trials and tribulations. For eighteen years, Gail taught three-year-old preschool at Chapin Baptist Church in Chapin, South Carolina. She also worked many years as the Volunteer Coordinator for Meals on Wheels in Columbia, South Carolina.

She found inspiration to begin writing after the loss of both her daughter, Laura, and her son-in-law, Mark. They left behind three children, ages seven, twelve, and seventeen. Gail immediately moved from playing the role of a grandmother to the role of a mother. She believes that her time working with children prepared her to become a full-time single parent to three children at the age of 68. While this can be a tremendous challenge for her at times, she makes it through each day because of her faith in God. She writes to help children during times of grief.

Gail has lived all over the United States, including Michigan, Arizona, and South Carolina. She currently resides in Myrtle Beach. In her free time, Gail is very artistic and enjoys crafting. She has an Etsy shop where she sells wedding bouquets, boutonnieres, corsages, and more. She has a creative spirit and a zest for creating beautiful things.

CPSIA information can be obtained
at www.ICGtesting.com
Printed in the USA
BVHW022358261121
622522BV00037B/684